AGS CLASSICS

CLASSROOM READING PLAYS

D1081887

A CHRISTMAS CAROL

Charles Dickens

Adapted by Joanne Suter

AGS®

AMERICAN GUIDANCE SERVICE, INC.
Circle Pines, Minnesota 55014-1796

AGS CLASSROOM READING PLAYS

SHAKESPEARE 2

KING LEAR
OTHELLO
THE TEMPEST
THE TAMING OF THE SHREW

BRITISH LITERATURE 2

A CHRISTMAS CAROL
JANE EYRE
ROBINSON CRUSOE
THE MUTINY ON BOARD H.M.S. BOUNTY

AMERICAN LITERATURE 2

THE LAST OF THE MOHICANS
TOM SAWYER
THE PRINCE AND THE PAUPER
A CONNECTICUT YANKEE IN KING ARTHUR'S COURT

Cover Illustration: Jun Lofamia
Cover Designer: Ina McInnis

ISBN 0-7854-0555-0
Product Number 40260
Printed in the United States of America
A 0 9 8 7 6 5 4 3 2 1

A Christmas Carol

Cast of Characters
(in order of first appearance)

NARRATOR

FIRST LONDONER

SECOND LONDONER

EBENEZER SCROOGE

BOB CRATCHIT

FRED

GENTLEMAN

GHOST OF JACOB
MARLEY

GHOST OF CHRISTMAS
PAST

FAN

YOUNG SCROOGE

FEZZIWIG

LADY GUEST

BELLE

HUSBAND

GHOST OF CHRISTMAS
PRESENT

MRS. CRATCHIT

MARTHA CRATCHIT

PETER CRATCHIT

TINY TIM

PARTY GUESTS

FRED'S WIFE

FIRST GUEST

GHOST OF CHRISTMAS
YET TO COME

FIRST BUSINESSMAN

SECOND BUSINESSMAN

MAN IN STORE

MEG

BOY

A Christmas Carol

ACT I

Scene 1. London, Scrooge's office

NARRATOR Our story begins on a cold Christmas Eve in nineteenth-century London. As the first scene opens, the hour is late. We see a stingy old man named Ebenezer Scrooge and his clerk, Bob Cratchit. They are still at work in a dark, chilly office. Outside, snow is falling and the wind is blowing. Many people rush by on last-minute Christmas errands. None of these happy people are too cold to wish the others a merry Christmas! Yet it seems warmer *outside* than in Scrooge's drafty office!

FIRST LONDONER *(voice heard from outside)* A merry Christmas to you!

SECOND LONDONER *(from outside)* Good wishes for the New Year!

SCROOGE *(grumbling)* You didn't put more coal on the fire, did you, Cratchit?

CRATCHIT Oh, no, sir.

SCROOGE Good! Make sure you don't. And keep your eye off that clock, too!

CRATCHIT *(to himself)* Will this day *never* end? It's Christmas Eve! I have much to do tonight.

NARRATOR Scrooge sits at his desk, counting coins. Then a smiling young man opens the door. It is Scrooge's nephew, Fred.

FRED *(jolly)* A merry Christmas, Uncle!

SCROOGE *(frowning)* Bah! Humbug!

FRED *(laughing)* Christmas, a humbug, uncle? You don't mean that, I'm sure!

SCROOGE Ha! A man who goes about with "Merry Christmas" on his lips is a fool! He should be boiled in his own pudding! Then he should be buried with a branch of holly stuck in his heart! Just look at *you!* Why should you be merry? You're a poor man!

FRED *(laughing)* And why are you such a grouch, then? You're a very rich man! Oh, Uncle, Christmas is the only day of the year when people truly open their hearts. You're right that Christmas has never put a penny in my pocket. But I believe it has done me good! That's why I say, God bless it!

CRATCHIT Hooray! Hooray!

SCROOGE *(shouting)* Quiet! Another sound from you, Cratchit, and you can celebrate Christmas by losing your job!

FRED *(still friendly)* Don't be angry, Uncle. I want you to come and have Christmas dinner with us tomorrow.

SCROOGE I will not! Christmas is a lot of humbug! Good-bye!

FRED *(disappointed)* Good-bye then, Uncle. And a happy holiday to you anyway!

NARRATOR As Fred leaves, another gentleman enters Scrooge's office.

GENTLEMAN I am collecting money for the poor, sir. Many have no homes and very little food! They could use some extra cheer on Christmas!

SCROOGE *(rudely)* Why, you can see that *I* don't make merry myself at Christmas, sir. And I can't afford to make lazy people merry! Are there no prisons? Are there no workhouses? That's where they belong!

GENTLEMAN *(upset)* Surely *not*, sir! Many people would rather die than go there!

SCROOGE *(coldly)* If they would rather die, then let them do so. There are too many people in the world as it is!

GENTLEMAN A merry Christmas to you anyway, sir!

NARRATOR The gentleman leaves. There is nothing more he can say. At last it is time to close the office. Bob Cratchit blows out his candle and puts on his hat.

SCROOGE I suppose you'll be wanting the whole day off tomorrow!

CRATCHIT Why, y-yes, sir.

SCROOGE *(sternly)* It's a bad reason to rob a man's pocket every twenty-fifth of December! Make sure to be here early the next day.

CRATCHIT *(happily)* Yes, sir! Indeed I will, sir. A merry Christmas to you, Mr. Scrooge.

SCROOGE Bah! Humbug!

Scene 2. Scrooge's home

Narrator After a lonely supper at a nearby shop, Scrooge starts home. Walking along the dark streets, he finally reaches an old building. Scrooge lives alone in rooms there. The place had once been the home of his partner, Jacob Marley. But Marley has been dead for seven years now. Scrooge puts the key in the lock, but then he is startled. The door knocker in front of him seems to *glow!*

Scrooge *(blinking)* What's this? Can it be?

Narrator Marley's *face* seems to appear on the brass knocker! As Scrooge stands staring, the face fades. Soon he can see only the dull, brass knocker.

Scrooge *(blinking again)* Bah! I *couldn't* have seen Marley's face. My mind must be playing tricks on me!

Narrator Once inside, Scrooge quickly lights a candle. He locks the door behind him and starts up the stairs.

Scrooge *(to himself)* It was nothing!

Narrator When he reaches his bedroom, Scrooge puts on his robe and nightcap. He makes a small fire and pulls a chair up to the fireplace. But just as he sits down, a small bell in the room begins to ring.

(Bell rings.)

Scrooge *(listening)* What's that?

Narrator At first, the ringing is soft. But it slowly grows louder and louder. Then other bells in the house begin to ring as well. Suddenly the bells stop ringing. Now Scrooge hears the clanking of chains!

(Chains clank.)

Scrooge *(frightened)* I didn't hear anything. It's *nothing!* I won't believe it.

Narrator But the clanking of chains is getting louder! The sound seems to be coming up the stairs and toward Scrooge's room! Then, right there in the light thrown by the fire, Scrooge sees the ghost of Jacob Marley! The ghost is draped in heavy chains.

Scrooge *(nervous) Who are you?*

Ghost of Jacob Marley *(in a hollow voice)* In life, I was your partner Jacob Marley.

Scrooge *(surprised)* But you are in chains, Marley. Tell me why!

Narrator Now Scrooge can see that Marley's chains are made of cash boxes, keys, padlocks, and heavy steel purses.

Ghost of Jacob Marley *(sadly)* I wear the chains I made myself—during my life! Is it so strange to you, Scrooge? *You* are making such a chain yourself . . . only yours is already far heavier than mine.

Scrooge *(frightened)* What do you mean? I don't understand, Jacob! You were always a good businessman.

Narrator At those words, the spirit lets out a fearful cry. He rattles his chains.

Ghost of Jacob Marley *(moaning) Business?* I never knew what my business truly was. *People* were my business! *Charity* and *kindness* were my business! But I thought only of money! Now I must forever walk the earth and see the things I *might* have done while I was alive. *Beware, Ebenezer!* The same thing will happen to you!

Narrator At this, Scrooge feels a cold stab of fear. He falls on his knees. Marley points at him with a long, white finger.

Ghost of Jacob Marley This is why I have come, Ebenezer. Listen closely! My time is almost gone.

Scrooge I'm listening, Jacob! But don't be too hard on me.

Ghost of Jacob Marley *(seriously)* I am here tonight to warn you. You do not have to follow the way that I have gone. Tonight you will be visited by three spirits. The first will come tomorrow when the clock strikes one. The second will come the next night at the same hour. The third will arrive the next night after the last stroke of twelve. You will see me no more—but remember what has passed between us!

Narrator At that, Marley's ghost starts to fade. It slowly floats backward through the window and out into the night. Scrooge looks out the window. In the air, he sees other figures wearing chains. All of them are crying and wailing.

Scrooge *(whispering)* Those faces—I have seen them before! Why, I *knew* many of these spirits when they lived!

Narrator Then the spirits and their wailing voices fade from the night sky. Now the night is as silent as it was before. Frightened and tired, Scrooge goes straight to bed. He falls into a restless sleep.

ACT II

Scene 1. Scrooge's room

SCROOGE *(sleepily)* Wh-what's that? Is there a bell ringing?

NARRATOR When the clock strikes one, Scrooge hears a deep, dull sound. Lights flash, and the curtains of his bed are pulled back. Sitting up quickly, Scrooge finds himself face to face with an unearthly visitor. It is a strange figure—something like a child, yet something like an old man. White hair hangs about the figure's neck and down its back. Yet the face has not a wrinkle upon it. The arms are long, and the hands look very strong. The spirit wears a white robe and carries a branch of holly. Bright light shines all around it. But under its arm, the spirit carries a hat that can dim the rays.

SCROOGE *(afraid)* Are you the spirit I was told to expect?

GHOST OF CHRISTMAS PAST *(in a deep voice)* Yes. I am the Ghost of Christmas Past.

SCROOGE *Long* past?

GHOST OF CHRISTMAS PAST No, *your* past.

SCROOGE *(curious)* Why do you carry your cap? Put it on, sir.

GHOST OF CHRISTMAS PAST What? Would you so soon put out the light I have to give? It is people like you whose bad feelings *made* this cap. Such people sometimes force me to dim my light!

SCROOGE I meant no harm. Tell me why you are here.

GHOST OF CHRISTMAS PAST I have come to help save you. Rise, Ebenezer Scrooge. Walk with me!

Narrator But as the spirit moves toward the window, Scrooge holds back.

Scrooge You are going to lead me out the window? But I am a *man*, not a spirit! I will fall!

Ghost of Christmas Past Oh no! Just a touch of my hand upon your heart will hold you up!

Narrator Amazed, Scrooge feels the spirit's hand touch his chest. Then Scrooge follows the spirit right into the night sky!

Scene 2. A country village

Narrator Soon Scrooge and the Ghost of Christmas Past come to a street in a small country village. The darkness disappears. Now it is a clear, cold winter day. There is snow on the ground.

Ghost of Christmas Past Look! Do you remember this place?

Scrooge *(excited) Remember* it? I could walk about this place with my eyes closed. I was born here!

Narrator The spirit points at schoolboys on their way home for the holidays. Their Christmas greetings to each other fill the air. Scrooge tries to call out to the boys, but they do not hear him.

Ghost of Christmas Past What you see are shadows of things that *have been*. The people here can neither see us nor hear us.

Narrator Scrooge and the spirit enter an old school building. There they find a dark room full of empty desks. At one desk, a lonely boy sits reading.

Ghost of Christmas Past Only one child was left here alone. That was *you*, Scrooge!

Narrator Scrooge sits down at one of the desks. He weeps to see himself as he used to be.

Ghost of Christmas Past *Look*, Scrooge! Your books made good friends. But you would have traded them all for one *real* friend, wouldn't you?

Scrooge *(sadly)* Poor, lonely boy! It's too late now, but . . .

Ghost of Christmas Past What is the matter?

Scrooge Oh, I just remembered something that happened today. There was a boy singing a Christmas carol at my door. I wish I had given him something—that's all.

Narrator The spirit smiles at this. Then the spirit puts on its hat, shutting out the light. When the spirit takes off its hat again, it is another Christmas. The schoolroom is even darker now. The boy Scrooge is older. This time he is not reading, but walking sadly back and forth.

Ghost of Christmas Past Left alone again, weren't you? The other boys have all gone home for the holidays.

Narrator Then the boy they are watching hears a sound at the schoolroom door. A little girl, much younger than he, comes running in.

Fan *Surprise!* I have come to bring you home, dear brother!

Young Scrooge *Home*, little Fan?

Fan Yes . . . home *for good!* One night Father spoke so gently to me that I was not afraid. I asked him if you might come home—and he said *yes!* Oh, Ebenezer, Father is so much kinder than he used to be! And we're all going to be together this Christmas! We'll have the best time in the world!

Ghost of Christmas Past Your sister was always a shy girl, wasn't she? She was one who could not stand being treated badly. And she had a good heart, too, did she not?

Scrooge You are right, spirit. Little Fan was always sweet
and good.

Ghost of Christmas Past She had a son, didn't she—
before she died?

Scrooge Yes . . . my nephew Fred.

Narrator At the memory of Fred's visit, a tear falls on
Scrooge's cheek.

Scene 3. London

Narrator Scrooge and the spirit leave the village school
behind them. Now they are back in the busy city. From
the decorated shop windows, it is clear that it is
Christmastime again.

Ghost of Christmas Past Come, Ebenezer! Another
Christmas is before us!

Narrator It is evening, and the street lamps have been
lighted. The spirit stops Scrooge before a shop door.

Ghost of Christmas Past Do you know this place?

Scrooge *(excited) Know* it? This was the first place I ever
worked! Dick Wilkins and I were apprentices here.

Narrator   Scrooge and the spirit move inside. They see a
chubby old gentleman. He is sitting on a high stool,
working at a desk. A tiny smile is on his lips.

Scrooge Why, it's old Fezziwig!

Fezziwig The clock strikes the hour! Yo ho, my boys—
Ebenezer Scrooge! Dick Wilkins! No more work tonight,
for it's Christmas Eve! Up with the shutters! Clear the
room! All must be ready!

Narrator Two young men jump at Fezziwig's order. Shutters go up—one, two, three! Every piece of furniture that can be moved is pushed aside in a minute! The floor is swept.

Fezziwig Ho there, Dick! Step lively, Ebenezer!

Narrator Piles of logs are heaped on the fire. Laughing young people spread a Christmas feast upon tables. It seems that a party is about to begin.

Fezziwig Nothing could be better than this! Come in, everyone! Merry Christmas!

Narrator And in comes a crowd of young clerks, one after another. It is a happy place to be on Christmas Eve! Then in comes a fiddler. The dancing is about to begin!

Lady Guest A wonderful party!

Fezziwig Thank you, all! We'll have an even better one next year!

Narrator The young Scrooge in this scene acts like a different man. He is enjoying everything! But soon, the dancing figures start to fade. Finally, Scrooge and the spirit are left alone in the empty room. But the light of that Christmas past is still bright!

Ghost of Christmas Past It did not take much to make those folks happy. And *you*, Ebenezer—you had as much fun as any of them!

Scrooge *(sadly)* True. But I see now that it was Fezziwig who *made* us happy—and that was worth a fortune!

Narrator Then Scrooge falls silent. His head hangs down.

Ghost of Christmas Past What is the matter?

Scrooge I just wish that I could say a word or two to my clerk, Bob Cratchit, right now.

Ghost of Christmas Past My time grows short! We must move on. Quickly!

Scene 4. A room decorated for Christmas

NARRATOR Now Scrooge sees yet another Christmas. This time he is a young man talking to a lovely young lady. But there are tears in her eyes! Her tears sparkle in the glowing Christmas lights.

BELLE I'm sorry, Ebenezer. I cannot marry you. It seems that another idol has taken my place in your heart.

YOUNG SCROOGE *(confused)* What do you mean, Belle? *What* other idol?

BELLE *(sadly)* A golden one. Your love for me is not as great as your love of money. But I will always love the person you *used* to be!

SCROOGE *(crying out)* Show me no more!

GHOST OF CHRISTMAS PAST But I *must!* There is one picture left.

NARRATOR Scrooge is forced to watch as the light of Christmas Past shows him one last scene. Now Scrooge sees a pleasant family, sharing Christmas Eve. The woman is his lost love. She is a mother now, happily sitting with her husband.

BELLE *(smiling)* The children are finally asleep, my dear.

HUSBAND Belle, I saw an old friend of yours this afternoon.

BELLE Who?

HUSBAND Mr. Scrooge. I passed his office and saw him through the window. He had a very unhappy look on his face.

BELLE *(upset) How sad!*

HUSBAND He's quite alone in the world, I believe.

SCROOGE *(almost in tears)* Oh, spirit, I must leave this place. I can bear no more.

GHOST OF CHRISTMAS PAST These scenes should not surprise you. They are only the shadows of things past. Do not blame *me* for what you see!

SCROOGE *(in pain)* Take me back! Leave me alone!

NARRATOR Upset by all he has seen, Scrooge strikes out at the spirit. He tries to pull its hat down. He would do *anything* to shut out the light! It has shown him too much! All of a sudden, Ebenezer Scrooge feels very, very tired.

ACT III

Scene 1. Scrooge's room

NARRATOR Back in his own bedroom, Scrooge wakes up with a start. But he is still very tired. In a few minutes, he sinks back into a heavy sleep.

Scrooge wakes again when the clock strikes one. He knows it is time for his second visitor. Peeping from his bedcovers, he sees a strange light fill the room. Then all goes dark and a booming voice rings out.

GHOST OF CHRISTMAS PRESENT *(loudly) Ebenezer Scrooge! Ebenezer Scrooge!*

Narrator Scrooge's eyes snap open. What a sight he sees! It is *his* room—but so changed he almost does not know it. The walls are hung with holly, mistletoe, and ivy. A fresh fire is blazing in the fireplace, and a Christmas feast has been set out.

Ghost of Christmas Present *(a booming voice)* Welcome, Scrooge! You must get to know me better! I am the ghost of Christmas present! Look upon me.

Narrator A giant holding a glowing torch sits upon Scrooge's own couch! The light from the torch makes the whole room glow.

Ghost of Christmas Present *(booming)* Have you ever seen the likes of me before?

Scrooge Never! Please, spirit! Take me where you will! I am slowly learning from what I see. Tonight, if you have something to teach me, I will try my best to understand.

Ghost of Christmas Present Touch my robe!

Narrator Scrooge reaches out and holds fast to the ghost's sleeve.

Scene 2. A small London house

Narrator Suddenly, Scrooge finds himself inside a small and shabby house. The neighborhood is in a very poor part of London.

Scrooge Why, this is the home of my clerk, Bob Cratchit!

Narrator Mrs. Cratchit, her daughter Belinda, and her son Peter are all busy preparing Christmas dinner. Their clothes look old and worn, but their smiles are shining. Soon, two smaller Cratchit children come rushing into the room. They are shouting with joy.

MRS. CRATCHIT *(lovingly)* Children, what is keeping your father and Tiny Tim? And where can Martha be?

MARTHA *(entering)* Here I am, Mother! We had a lot of work to finish before I could get away.

MRS. CRATCHIT Never mind, dear Martha—just so long as you're here! Sit down in front of the fire and warm yourself. Oh! Here come Father and Tiny Tim. Let's surprise them!

PETER Hide, Martha, hide!

NARRATOR Martha hides herself behind the door just in time. A moment later, Bob and Tiny Tim come in.

CRATCHIT *(looking around)* Why, where's our Martha?

MRS. CRATCHIT *(pretending to be sad)* Not coming, I'm afraid.

CRATCHIT *(upset)* Not coming—on Christmas Day?

NARRATOR At these words, Martha runs out to hug her father. Even as a joke, she cannot bear to see a sad look on his face.

MARTHA *(laughing)* Dear father!

NARRATOR The two youngest Cratchit children rush up to Tiny Tim. All three go off to smell the Christmas pudding as it cooks.

MRS. CRATCHIT How did little Tim behave in church?

CRATCHIT As good as gold—and better! Brave little fellow! And doesn't he have the strangest ideas? He said he hoped that people in church saw him, because he was a cripple . . .

NARRATOR At that, Bob's voice breaks. He is about to cry. The he pulls himself together and goes on.

CRATCHIT He said it might be good for them to remember who made cripples walk and blind men see—especially on Christmas Day!

NARRATOR The family sets out their poor little Christmas dinner. But this Christmas day is not a sad one for the Cratchits. Their simple meal has been prepared with love—and everyone has something good to say.

CRATCHIT I do believe this is the best meal we have ever had!

NARRATOR The flaming pudding appears at the end of the meal. When everyone claps to see it, Mrs. Cratchit beams at her family. At last dinner is done. Now the family gathers around the fireplace for a glass of hot punch. Before they drink, Bob Cratchit offers a toast.

CRATCHIT *(joyfully)* A merry Christmas to us all, my dears. God bless us!

MRS. CRATCHIT God bless us!

NARRATOR Tiny Tim is the last to speak. He is sitting on a little stool, close to his father's side.

TINY TIM God bless us, every one!

NARRATOR As Scrooge watches the happy family, he whispers to the spirit.

SCROOGE Tell me, spirit, the boy looks sick. Will Tiny Tim live?

GHOST OF CHRISTMAS PRESENT I see an empty chair, and a crutch without its owner. If these shadows are not changed by the future, the child will die!

SCROOGE Oh, no!

GHOST OF CHRISTMAS PRESENT Why do *you* care? You've already said that there are too many people in the world!

NARRATOR At the spirit's words, Scrooge hangs his head. Then he raises it again when he hears his name.

CRATCHIT Let's toast Mr. Scrooge now, my dears! After all, he is the man who gave us this feast!

MRS. CRATCHIT *(disgusted)* Gave us this feast, indeed! I wish he were here. I'd give him a piece of my mind to feast upon!

CRATCHIT *(alarmed)* Oh, no, my dear! Think of the children! Let us have only *kind* words spoken. After all, this is Christmas Day!

MRS. CRATCHIT *(grudgingly)* If you wish it so, Bob. Only on Christmas Day could I drink to the health of such a hard man. But here's to Mr. Scrooge! May he be merry and happy! *(shaking her head)* But I don't think the old grouch *can* be!

NARRATOR To please their father, the family makes the toast. But there is little good feeling in it. Scrooge's name has set a shadow over the party. But that shadow quickly passes and their joy returns. Then the little group slowly fades from sight. Scrooge keeps his eyes upon them until the last.

Scene 3. The home of Scrooge's nephew

NARRATOR Again, Scrooge flies away with the spirit. He soon finds himself standing in the bright, warm home of his nephew. Fred and his wife are having a Christmas party. Many of their young friends are dancing and playing games. Scrooge sees that Fred is telling a story. The guests are all laughing. What's this? The story is about *him!*

FRED My old uncle said that Christmas was a humbug! And he *believed* it, too!

Guests Ha, ha! Ha, ha, ha, ha!

Narrator For the first time, Scrooge sees the face of Fred's beautiful wife. She is angry!

Fred's Wife *(upset)* How could *anyone* say such a thing, Fred?

First Guest I hear that old Scrooge is a very rich man.

Fred But his money is of no use to him, *or* to others! What good does it do? I asked him to come and have Christmas dinner with us—but he wouldn't hear of it! Just see the fun he misses! Do not mock him, friends. I feel sorry for him!

Narrator Then, in the true spirit of the season, Fred makes a toast to his Uncle Scrooge. He raises his glass.

Fred A merry Christmas and a happy New Year to the old man, wherever he is!

Guests Here, here! To Uncle Scro-o-o-oge!

Narrator The happy group plays games for the rest of the evening. Scrooge enjoys the fun, though no one else knows it.

Scrooge *(to himself)* Deck the halls with boughs of holly! Fa la la la la. . . .

Narrator When the spirit says that it is time to go, Scrooge begs like a child to stay. He wants to enjoy the whole party. Then he notices that the spirit's hair has turned gray.

Scrooge Gray hair? Do spirits' lives pass so quickly?

Ghost of Christmas Present My life here is very short. It ends tonight at midnight. Hurry now, the time is near!

Narrator Then Scrooge sees something moving beneath the spirit's robe.

Scrooge Spirit, what is that behind your robe?

GHOST OF CHRISTMAS PRESENT These are all the children of the world who are poor and ignorant.

SCROOGE *(concerned)* Have they no home? Is there no one to help them?

NARRATOR For the second time, the spirit makes Scrooge hang his head. Again, he does this by repeating some of Scrooge's own words!

GHOST OF CHRISTMAS PRESENT *(mocking Scrooge's voice) Are there no prisons? Are there no workhouses?*

NARRATOR Fred's house begins to fade. Scrooge finds himself feeling very tired again.

ACT IV

Scene 1. London

NARRATOR Somewhere a clock strikes twelve. Out of the darkness, Scrooge sees another spirit coming toward him. This spirit wears a black robe that hides its head, face, and form. Nothing can be seen but its bony hand. Scrooge is terrified. He knows it is the ghost of Christmas Yet to Come! The spirit says not a word. It only nods its head and points with its finger.

SCROOGE *(in a shaky voice)* What are you about to show me? Things that have not yet happened but *could* happen in the future? Oh, spirit, have mercy! I hope to become another man from what I was! But I know that you are here to do me good . . . so lead on!

NARRATOR The city seems to spring up all around them. They are in the Merchants' Exchange, where London's businesspeople meet.

FIRST BUSINESSMAN I hear the old skinflint died last night.

SECOND BUSINESSMAN Left his money to his company, I guess.

FIRST BUSINESSMAN Who will go to the funeral?

SECOND BUSINESSMAN Who would *want* to?

NARRATOR Scrooge knows that what he is seeing will take place in the future. Wondering who it is that died, he looks around for himself. But another man is in his usual place!

SCROOGE Hmmm. That's strange! Well, perhaps I have changed my ways by now. I am probably in a better place—a place that does good for people!

NARRATOR Then the spirit again points its bony finger. The Merchants' Exchange fades away.

Scene 2. A shop in a poor part of London

NARRATOR Still pointing its finger, the spirit shows Scrooge a poor, rundown part of the city. Crime and evil are no strangers here!

SCROOGE This is a terrible place! What am I to learn from this?

NARRATOR They follow a poor-looking woman. Carrying a heavy bundle, she sneaks into a hidden shop. The owner of this store buys and sells stolen goods. Meg, the poor woman, has come to sell some clothes she has stolen. Scrooge and the spirit listen.

MAN IN STORE So you've been to the dead man's place, Meg?

MEG Yes.

MAN IN STORE You took these things while he was still lying there?

Meg Yes—all of them!

Man in Store Well, let's see what you have. What are these woolen things?

Meg His blankets. *(laughing)* He won't catch cold without 'em, I guess! That fine shirt could have gone to waste. He might have been buried in it!

Man in Store And you took it off of him? Good job!

Narrator The man drops some coins into Meg's hand.

Meg That selfish old man gave nothing in life. Let him give something in death, say I!

Narrator Scrooge hears her next words in horror.

Meg His meanness drove everyone away. I don't think there was a soul who liked him.

Scrooge *(distressed)* Will she *never* stop talking? I won't hear anymore!

Meg A friend would have been with him on Christmas Eve. Instead, he died there all alone.

Scrooge *(shaking)* Spirit! The story of this man might be my own! My life has been like that.

Narrator The spirit gives no answer. The night grows very dark.

Scene 3. A dark room

Narrator Darkness is all around. One light shines on Scrooge and the Ghost of Christmas Yet to Come. Another shines on a bed. Pointing to a figure on the bed, the spirit seems to be telling Scrooge to draw back the cover. It seems that he wants to show Scrooge who is there!

Scrooge *(terrified)* No, spirit, I cannot do it! *(pleading)* *Please*, let us go from this fearful place! In leaving it, I shall not forget its lesson—I promise!

Narrator But the spirit continues to point.

Scrooge I *cannot* look on that face! Is there *anyone* in this town who feels sad about his death?

Narrator Like a dark wing, the spirit's robe moves. Then the lights go out.

Scene 4. Bob Cratchit's house

Narrator Finally, the spirit again brings Scrooge into the home of Bob Cratchit. This time Mrs. Cratchit sits sewing before the fire. With her are some of her children.

Mrs. Cratchit *(upset)* Your father is late.

Peter I'm worried about him, Mother. These last few evenings, he walks more slowly than ever.

Mrs. Cratchit *(sighing)* He used to walk very fast with Tiny Tim upon his shoulder! Do you remember, children?

Narrator Then the door opens, and Bob Cratchit walks in. Now he looks much sadder and much older.

Cratchit *(crying out)* How green a place his little grave is! Tim! My child!

Narrator Tears run down the father's face.

Cratchit None of us will ever forget Tiny Tim.

Scrooge Spirit! Something tells me that our parting moment is at hand. I know it, but I know not how.

Narrator Scrooge pauses. The question he hates to ask is on his lips.

SCROOGE *(slowly) Who was that man that died?*

NARRATOR But the spirit does not answer. Only the pointing finger shows Scrooge where they are going next.

Scene 5. Outside Scrooge's office

SCROOGE Why, this is my old office. My future self must be here!

NARRATOR But the spirit's hand is pointing down the road.

SCROOGE But my office is *here!* Why do you point away from it?

NARRATOR Yet the spirit's pointing finger does not move.

SCROOGE By all that's holy, I'll see for myself!

NARRATOR Scrooge runs to the office window. Peeking inside, he sees that it is an office still. But the man sitting at his desk . . . is *not* Ebenezer Scrooge!

SCROOGE My office is the same, but someone else has taken my place!

Scene 6. A graveyard

NARRATOR Scrooge goes back to the spirit. Now he follows him to an iron gate. Passing through the gate, the spirit leads the way through an old graveyard at the side of a church. Some of the graves are walled in by houses and covered with weeds. These are the graves of the forgotten—people no one cares about. The spirit stands among the gravestones and points one of them out. Scrooge cannot look at it.

Scrooge *(shaking with fear)* Oh, spirit, answer me! Are these the shadows of things that will be? Or are they shadows of things that *might* be?

Narrator Still the silent spirit points. At last, Scrooge draws near to read the gravestone.

Scrooge Tell me, spirit! Am *I* that man laid out upon that bed?

Narrator The finger points from the grave to Scrooge and back again.

Scrooge But I am not the man I was! I *will not* be that man again! Why show me this if I am past all hope?

Narrator For the first time the spirit's hand seems to shake a bit.

Scrooge Tell me, please! How can I change the shadows I have just seen? I want to *live!* I want to become a *better person!*

Narrator Now the spirit's hand shakes harder.

Scrooge Hear me, spirit! I promise to honor Christmas in my heart—and keep it all the year! Please, do not let these sad things happen!

Narrator As Scrooge pleads, the spirit begins to shrink away.

Scrooge Come back, spirit! You must help me! You *must!*

Narrator But the spirit grows smaller and smaller. At last it is no bigger than a bedpost—and then it is gone!

ACT V

Scene 1. Scrooge's room

SCROOGE What . . .? How . . .? Where . . .?

NARRATOR Scrooge wakes up. Everything in his room is the same—but he knows that he has been saved. He has been granted the time to make many changes!

SCROOGE *(joyfully, to himself)* Oh, thank you, Jacob Marley! Heaven and Christmastime be praised for this! I am truly grateful! See, I'm *dancing!* I'm as light as a feather and as happy as an angel! Marley's ghost came through that door right over there. That couch is where the Ghost of Christmas Present sat! But it's all right now! It's all true! It all happened! *(laughing loudly)* Ha! Ha! Ha! I don't know what day it is! Or how long I was among the spirits! But who cares?

NARRATOR Scrooge flings up the window, and puts out his head. He hears church bells ringing.

SCROOGE What a wonderful sound! Oh, it's beautiful! *Beautiful!*

NARRATOR A boy is passing by on the street below. He looks up as Scrooge calls out to him.

SCROOGE What day is it, my fine fellow?

BOY *Today?* Why, it's Christmas Day, sir!

SCROOGE *(joyfully) Christmas!* I haven't missed it. The spirits have done it all in one night! *(shouting down)* Young man, have they sold the prize turkey in the shop around the corner?

BOY What? The turkey that's as big as me? No, sir! It's hanging there now.

SCROOGE Go and buy it, then. Have the butcher bring it here, and I'll give you a shilling.

Narrator The boy is off like a shot.

Scrooge *(shouting after him)* Be back in less than five minutes, and I'll give you *two times* as much!

Narrator Scrooge runs to his desk and quickly writes an address on a card. In a moment, the door knocker clangs.

Scrooge *(to himself)* I'll send the turkey to Bob Cratchit's. *(calling out the window) I'll be right down!* Why look— that turkey is *twice* the size of Tiny Tim! The butcher and the boy together couldn't carry that big bird to Camden Town! I'll get you a cab, and pay for it too!

Scene 2. A London street

Narrator Dressed in his best clothes, Scrooge walks to church. On the street, he sees a gentleman he remembers.

Scrooge *(in high spirits)* Here, my good sir! Take this money. Yesterday I turned you down when you wanted to help the poor and needy. But today . . .

Gentleman *(amazed)* Such an *amount!* My dear Mr. Scrooge, are you sure of this?

Scrooge *(joyfully)* I am. Not a cent less! A great many back payments have to be made.

Scene 3. The house of Scrooge's nephew

Narrator After church, Scrooge hurries to the house of his nephew, Fred. He doesn't want to be late for Christmas dinner! Fred and his wife greet him with surprise.

Fred Uncle! You *did* come for Christmas dinner after all!

FRED'S WIFE Uncle Scrooge, it's so nice to finally meet you.

SCROOGE Bless you both, my dears!

NARRATOR Fred's house is filled with music and laughter. And Scrooge is the life of the Christmas party.

SCROOGE *(singing)* Fa-la-la-la-la, la-la-la-la!

Scene 4. Scrooge's office

NARRATOR The next morning, Scrooge arrives at his office early. Just as Scrooge hoped, Bob Cratchit is a few minutes late. Scrooge frowns at him as he rushes in.

CRATCHIT *(nervous)* I'm sorry to be late, sir. I'll never let it happen again!

SCROOGE *(gruffly)* I've had quite enough of this, Bob Cratchit! And so . . . I am about to *raise your salary!*

NARRATOR The poor clerk cannot believe his ears! He is speechless!

SCROOGE We'll talk this over right now—with a cup of holiday punch! You've done good work for me for many years, Bob. Now I want to help you and your family.

NARRATOR Ebenezer Scrooge remains true to his word. He does everything he said he would. In time, he becomes a second father to Tiny Tim, who does not die after all. As a matter of fact, Scrooge becomes as good a man as the good old city of London ever knew! For the rest of his life, people always say that no one knows how to keep Christmas better than Ebenezer Scrooge!

May that be truly said of all of us! And, as Tiny Tim once said. . .

TINY TIM God bless us, every one!